What the World Needs

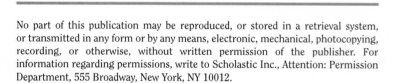

Copyright © 1999 by Scholastic Inc.
All rights reserved. Published by Scholastic Inc.

ISBN 0-439-15011-6

12 11 10 9 8 7 6 5 4 3 2 1   9/9 0/0 01 02 03 04

Printed in U.S.A.   14
First printing, October 1999

What the World Needs

Written and illustrated by fourth-grade students
of Mansfield Elementary Middle School in Mansfield, Louisiana

Mr. Kervin Campbell, Teacher

SCHOLASTIC INC.
New York   Toronto   London   Auckland   Sydney
Mexico City   New Delhi   Hong Kong

THE STORY BEHIND THE STORY OF
What the World Needs

What the World Needs was created by Mansfield Elementary Middle School's fourth-grade students after studying a unit on Character Counts, a newly introduced program to build character among students. We chose this title for our entry this year because the students were discussing what they think the world would need in order to make it a better place to live. The class brainstormed ideas. We compiled these ideas and came up with an entry for Kids Are Authors.

MANSFIELD ELEMENTARY MIDDLE SCHOOL
MISSION STATEMENT

All students will be:
Ready, willing, and able to learn for life.

*This year's entry is dedicated
to our wonderful school principal,
Mrs. P. Jalanivich,
because of all the love and dedication she gives
to the children, school, and community
in Mansfield, Louisiana.*

What the World Needs

is more chocolate factories.

What the World Needs

is more teachers like Mr. Campbell.

What the World Needs

is a cure for diseases.

What the World Needs

is more ice cream shops.

What the World Needs

is to keep highways and streets clean.

What the World Needs

is good quality family shows
on television.

What the World Needs

is more drug education programs.

Drugs

Destroy

What the World Needs

is for people of different cultures
to live in peace and harmony.

What the World Needs

is to help the homeless people
find homes.

What the World Needs

is for people to stop destroying the rain forests.

What the World Needs

is more libraries and museums.

What the World Needs

is to preserve and protect
our endangered species.

What the World Needs

is a lot of love from caring people.

KIDS ARE AUTHORS

Books written by children for children

The Kids Are Authors® Competition was established in 1986 to encourage children to read and to become involved in the creative process of writing. Since then, thousands of children have written and illustrated books as participants in the Kids Are Authors® Competition. The winning books in the annual competition are published by Scholastic Inc. and are distributed by Scholastic Book Fairs throughout the United States.

For more information: **Kids Are Authors**® Scholastic Book Fairs   PO Box 958411   Lake Mary, FL 32795-8411
Or visit our web site at: www.scholasticbookfairs.com